Dear Parents:

The objects hidden in the pictures of this book
are shown on the inside front and back covers.

Looking for Letters

Written by M.C. Leeka
Illustrated by Florie Freshman

Modern Publishing
A Division of Unisystems, Inc.
New York, New York 10022

We're looking for letters,
We're hot on the trail.
If we search on the farm,
I know we won't fail.

We'll begin at the barn,
Where they keep bales of hay.
And start off our search,
For our first letter "A".

We'll study the horses,
Inside of their stalls.
Do you think "B" and "C",
Might be hiding on walls?

Here comes the farmer,
To check on his cows.
To find "D" and "E",
We'll continue to browse.

We'll look in the cornfields,
There's so much to see.
We might come across,
Letters "F" and "G".

The strawberry field,
Is the next place we'll try.
We'll look for more letters,
Like "H" and "I".

We'll search in the meadows,
Where flocks of sheep graze.
We'll keep our eyes open,
To spot "J's" and "K's".

We studied the pigs,
But we might look again.
Letters "L" and "M",
Might be there in the pen.

We'll check out the garden,
Where vegetables grow.
We might have a chance,
To find "N" and "O".

We'll study the rooster,
And barn swallows, too.
We'll search everywhere,
To find "P" and "Q".

The chickens are scratching,
For food on the ground.
Letters "R" and "S",
Must be somewhere around.

We'll check out the geese,
And we might find a clue,
That will help in our search,
For "T" and for "U".

We'll follow the turkeys,
Who wander about.
Letters "V" and "W",
We must seek out.

There are acres and acres,
The farmer must plow.
Letter "X", letter "Y",
We must find now.

The farmer has rabbits,
He raises as pets.
We'll find letter "Z",
Long before the sun sets.

On our visit today, there was so much to see.
We were able to find letters "A" through "Z".
This day on the farm has been so much fun,
But our search is now over and so we must run!